This book is dedicated with love
to the miracles in my life . . .
my wondrous sons, Billy, Nik, and Ethan

by
BILL THOMSON

SCHOLASTIC INC.
New York Toronto London Auckland
Sydney Mexico City New Delhi Hong Kong

ISBN 978-0-545-39982-1

Copyright © 2010 by Bill Thomson. All rights reserved. Published by Scholastic Inc., 557 Broadway, New York, NY 10012, by arrangement with Marshall Cavendish Corporation. SCHOLASTIC and associated logos are trademarks and/or registered trademarks of Scholastic Inc.

12 11 10 9 8 7 6 5 4   20 21 22/0

Printed in the U.S.A.   40

First Scholastic printing, September 2011

Bill Thomson embraced traditional painting techniques and meticulously painted each illustration by hand, using acrylic paint and colored pencils. His illustrations are not photographs or computer generated images.

Book design by Michael Nelson
Editor: Margery Cuyler

Bill Thomson would like to give special thanks
GameTime for use of their extraordinary Dinos
Adventure Mates playground ride. He would also
to thank Margery Cuyler and Anahid Hampa
for making a dream come t